dick bruna

miffy
at the
seaside

World International

Father Bunny said one day

who wants to come with me

down to the dunes and sandy beach

and then to see the sea?

Me, me, said Miffy, that is great

hurrah, I'll go as well

and I shall take my bucket too

in case I find some shells.

Right, said her dad, then in you get

I'm giving you a ride

we shall be at the beach quite soon

while you are safe inside.

Miffy went riding through the dunes

oh, aren't they high, she said

and Father Bun said, I can see

the beach there, straight ahead.

They stopped beside a jolly tent

look, Miff, we're here at last

you pulled so hard, cried little Miff

we travelled very fast.

Then Miffy took off all her clothes

and put her swimsuit on

well, well, said Father Bunny, that

was very quickly done.

So build a great big fortress now

here is your seaside spade

and I will make quite sure the fort

is well and strongly made.

Then Miffy dug with all her might

and built a solid wall

you see the top of Miffy's head –

the wall was very tall.

When Miff had finished digging

in all the yellow sand

she went to look for lovely shells

her bucket in her hand.

Then Father Bun took Miffy

to paddle in the sea

and Miffy splashed her daddy

as wet as wet can be.

As soon as they were dry again

said Dad, we cannot stay

it's time for home now, Miffy dear

it's been a lovely day.

That is a shame, cried Miffy

I'm not at all tired, but

once she was sitting in the truck

her eyes were soon tight shut.

miffy's library

miffy
miffy goes to stay
miffy is crying
miffy's birthday
miffy at school
miffy's bicycle

miffy's dream
miffy at the zoo
miffy in hospital
miffy in the tent
miffy at the seaside
miffy in the snow

miffy goes flying
miffy at the playground
poppy pig
poppy pig is sick
boris on the mountain
boris in the snow

"nijntje aan zee"
Original text Dick Bruna 1988 © copyright Mercis Publishing BV.
Illustrations Dick Bruna © copyright Mercis BV 1988.
Published in Great Britain in 1997 by World International Ltd.,
Deanway Technology Centre, Wilmslow Road, Handforth, Cheshire SK9 3FB.
Original English translation © copyright Patricia Crampton 1996.
Publication licensed by Mercis Publishing BV, Amsterdam.
Printed by Sebald Sachsendruck Plauen, Germany. All rights reserved.
ISBN 0-7498-2989-3

WORLD